INNER REFLECTIONS

2001 Engagement Calendar

SELECTIONS FROM THE WRITINGS OF
PARAMAHANSA YOGANANDA

SELF-REALIZATION FELLOWSHIP

THE SCENERY OF MOUNTAINS PAINTED ON THE EVER-CHANGING AZURE CAN-
VAS OF THE SKY, THE MYSTERIOUS MECHANISM OF THE HUMAN BODY, THE ROSE,
THE GREEN GRASS CARPET, THE MAGNANIMITY OF SOULS, THE LOFTINESS OF
MINDS, THE DEPTH OF LOVE—ALL THESE THINGS REMIND US OF A GOD WHO IS
BEAUTIFUL AND NOBLE.

—*Paramahansa Yogananda*

IN THIS CALENDAR we are happy to share with you some of the divine beauty that
reveals itself through the myriad forms of life and through our interaction with the
world around us. Whether spread over the vast heavens or hidden in the exquisite del-
icacy of a tiny flower, that beauty is always beckoning, inviting us to look behind the
outward form and sense the presence of God within.

The photographs featured here are accompanied by selections from the writings of Paramahansa Yogananda, whose timeless and universal teachings have awakened
many, of all races, cultures, and creeds, to a deeper awareness of the One Reality that
sustains and unites us all. We hope that the thoughts and images in these pages will
bring you inspiration and encouragement in the days and weeks of the coming year.

Fisherman on Li River, Yangshuo, Guangxi Province, China   Photograph by Charles Crust

INTUITION IS LIKE A LIGHT,
A FLAME OF KNOWLEDGE, THAT COMES FROM THE SOUL.
IT POSSESSES ALL-SIDED POWER TO KNOW ALL THERE IS TO BE KNOWN.

— *Paramahansa Yogananda*

Ocean bottom lit by crack in sea ice, Antarctica   Photograph by Norbert Wu

January

s	m	t	w	t	f	s
	1	2	3	4	5	6
7	8	9	10	11	12	13
14	15	16	17	18	19	20
21	22	23	24	25	26	27
28	29	30	31			

January

1
monday

New Year's Day

2
tuesday

First Quarter ◑

3
wednesday

4
thursday

Bank Holiday (Scotland)

5
friday

Paramahansa Yogananda's Birthday

6
saturday

7
sunday

February

s	m	t	w	t	f	s
				1	2	3
4	5	6	7	8	9	10
11	12	13	14	15	16	17
18	19	20	21	22	23	24
25	26	27	28			

January

January
s m t w t f s
1 2 3 4 5 6
7 8 9 10 11 12 13
14 15 16 17 18 19 20
21 22 23 24 25 26 27
28 29 30 31

8
monday

9
tuesday

Total Lunar Eclipse   *Full Moon* ○

10
wednesday

11
thursday

12
friday

13
saturday

14
sunday

February
s m t w t f s
1 2 3
4 5 6 7 8 9 10
11 12 13 14 15 16 17
18 19 20 21 22 23 24
25 26 27 28

HAPPINESS LIES IN GIVING YOURSELF TIME TO THINK AND TO INTROSPECT.
BE ALONE ONCE IN A WHILE.

— *Paramahansa Yogananda*

Zebra at sunrise, Etosha National Park, Namibia   Photograph by Rob Nunnington/Oxford Scientific Films Ltd

AS WATER BY COOLING AND CONDENSATION BECOMES ICE,
SO THOUGHT BY CONDENSATION ASSUMES PHYSICAL FORM.
EVERYTHING IN THE UNIVERSE IS THOUGHT IN MATERIAL FORM.

—*Paramahansa Yogananda*

Shoreline ice, Kotzebue Sound, Alaska   Photograph by Pat O'Hara

January

	s	m	t	w	t	f	s
		1	2	3	4	5	6
	7	8	9	10	11	12	13
	14	15	16	17	18	19	20
	21	22	23	24	25	26	27
	28	29	30	31			

Martin Luther King, Jr. Day

Last Quarter ◗

January

15
monday

16
tuesday

17
wednesday

18
thursday

19
friday

20
saturday

21
sunday

February

s	m	t	w	t	f	s
				1	2	3
4	5	6	7	8	9	10
11	12	13	14	15	16	17
18	19	20	21	22	23	24
25	26	27	28			

January

January
s m t w t f s
1 2 3 4 5 6
7 8 9 10 11 12 13
14 15 16 17 18 19 20
21 22 23 24 25 26 27
28 29 30 31

22
monday

23
tuesday

24
wednesday

New Moon ●

25
thursday

26
friday

Australia Day (Aus.)

27
saturday

28
sunday

February
s m t w t f s
1 2 3
4 5 6 7 8 9 10
11 12 13 14 15 16 17
18 19 20 21 22 23 24
25 26 27 28

BE ENTHRONED IN THE CASTLE OF GOODNESS....
IF YOU CONTINUOUSLY ADD TO THE GOOD THINGS YOU CAN REMEMBER,
YOU WILL IN TIME REMEMBER THE GREATEST GOOD...AND THAT IS GOD.

—Paramahansa Yogananda

Waterfowl in moat at sunrise, Leeds Castle, Kent, England   Photograph by Raoul Slater

LIFE IS VAGRANT, APPEARING AND DISAPPEARING
LIKE A RIVER IN THE DESERT OF TIME....
TO THE WISE [DEATH] IS A TRANSITION TO A HIGHER STATE—
A PROMOTION TO HIGHER GRADES OF LIFE.

— *Paramahansa Yogananda*

Sand dunes, Namib Desert, Namibia   Photograph by Claudia duPlessis

January

s m t w t f s
    1 2 3 4 5 6
7 8 9 10 11 12 13
14 15 16 17 18 19 20
21 22 23 24 25 26 27
28 29 30 31

January/February

29
monday

30
tuesday

31
wednesday

1
thursday

First Quarter ◐

2
friday

3
saturday

4
sunday

February

s m t w t f s
          1 2 3
4 5 6 7 8 9 10
11 12 13 14 15 16 17
18 19 20 21 22 23 24
25 26 27 28

February

February
s m t w t f s
1 2 3
4 5 6 7 8 9 10
11 12 13 14 15 16 17
18 19 20 21 22 23 24
25 26 27 28

5
monday

6
tuesday

Waitangi Day (N.Z.)

7
wednesday

Full Moon ○

8
thursday

9
friday

10
saturday

11
sunday

March
s m t w t f s
1 2 3
4 5 6 7 8 9 10
11 12 13 14 15 16 17
18 19 20 21 22 23 24
25 26 27 28 29 30 31

LOVE NURTURES ALL THINGS THAT GROW; IT HARMONIZES AND UNITES.
— *Paramahansa Yogananda*

Amazonian lily pads, Sir Seewoosagur Ramgoolam Gardens, Mauritius   Photograph by David Lyons

[GOD] IS THE MIRROR OF SILENCE IN WHICH ALL CREATION IS REFLECTED.

— *Paramahansa Yogananda*

Reflection of alders surrounded by ice, Sweden   Photograph by Jan Töve Johansson / Planet Earth Pictures Ltd

February

s m t w t f s
            1 2 3
4 5 6 7 8 9 10
11 12 13 14 15 16 17
18 19 20 21 22 23 24
25 26 27 28

February

12
monday

Lincoln's Birthday

13
tuesday

14
wednesday

Last Quarter ◑   *Valentine's Day*

15
thursday

16
friday

17
saturday

18
sunday

March

s m t w t f s
            1 2 3
4 5 6 7 8 9 10
11 12 13 14 15 16 17
18 19 20 21 22 23 24
25 26 27 28 29 30 31

February

19
monday

February
s m t w t f s
1 2 3
4 5 6 7 8 9 10
11 12 13 14 15 16 17
18 19 20 21 22 23 24
25 26 27 28

President's Day

20
tuesday

21
wednesday

22
thursday

Washington's Birthday

23
friday

New Moon ●

24
saturday

25
sunday

March
s m t w t f s
1 2 3
4 5 6 7 8 9 10
11 12 13 14 15 16 17
18 19 20 21 22 23 24
25 26 27 28 29 30 31

THE WHOLE WORLD IS PULSING WITH THE POWER OF GOD:
INDESCRIBABLE, INFINITE HAPPINESS.

— *Paramahansa Yogananda*

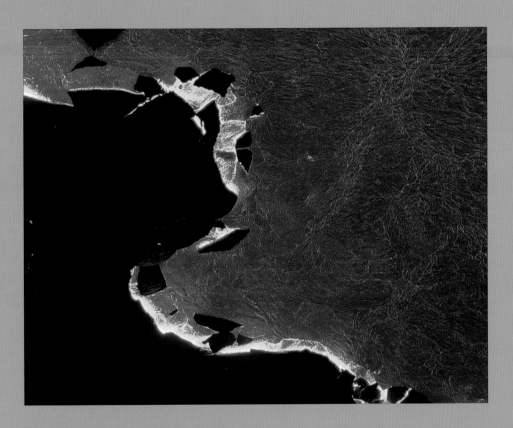

Lava in Pu'u O'o vent, Kilauea volcano, Hawaii   Photograph by G. Brad Lewis

A PEACE-CRYSTALLIZED INDIVIDUAL REMAINS RADIANTLY SERENE
EVEN WHEN TRIALS BESET HIM FROM ALL SIDES.

— *Paramahansa Yogananda*

Colors in ice, Hamar, Norway   Photograph by Asle Hjellbrekke

February

s m t w t f s
            1 2 3
4 5 6 7 8 9 10
11 12 13 14 15 16 17
18 19 20 21 22 23 24
25 26 27 28

February/March

26
monday

27
tuesday

28
wednesday

1
thursday

St. David's Day (Wales)

2
friday

First Quarter ◖

3
saturday

4
sunday

March

s m t w t f s
            1 2 3
4 5 6 7 8 9 10
11 12 13 14 15 16 17
18 19 20 21 22 23 24
25 26 27 28 29 30 31

March

March

s	m	t	w	t	f	s
				1	2	3
4	5	6	7	8	9	10
11	12	13	14	15	16	17
18	19	20	21	22	23	24
25	26	27	28	29	30	31

5
monday

6
tuesday

7
wednesday

Paramahansa Yogananda's Mahasamadhi

8
thursday

9
friday

Sri Yukteswar's Mahasamadhi   *Full Moon* ○

10
saturday

11
sunday

April

s	m	t	w	t	f	s
1	2	3	4	5	6	7
8	9	10	11	12	13	14
15	16	17	18	19	20	21
22	23	24	25	26	27	28
29	30					

YOU ARE INFINITE.
NOTHING IS SO IMPORTANT TO YOU AS TO KNOW THIS TRUTH.

— *Paramahansa Yogananda*

Horsehead Nebula, Orion constellation   Photograph by Kitt Peak Observatory, Arizona/Photo Researchers, Inc.

BECOME THE BUTTERFLY OF ETERNITY!
DECORATE YOUR WINGS OF REALIZATION WITH NATURE'S INFINITE CHARMS.

— *Paramahansa Yogananda*

Silvery blue butterfly, Camassia, Hornby Island, British Columbia, Canada   Photograph by Adam Gibbs

March

s	m	t	w	t	f	s
				1	2	3
4	5	6	7	8	9	10
11	12	13	14	15	16	17
18	19	20	21	22	23	24
25	26	27	28	29	30	31

March

12
monday

13
tuesday

14
wednesday

15
thursday

16
friday

Last Quarter ◑

17
saturday

St. Patrick's Day

18
sunday

April

s	m	t	w	t	f	s
1	2	3	4	5	6	7
8	9	10	11	12	13	14
15	16	17	18	19	20	21
22	23	24	25	26	27	28
29	30					

March

March
s m t w t f s
                1 2 3
4 5 6 7 8 9 10
11 12 13 14 15 16 17
18 19 20 21 22 23 24
25 26 27 28 29 30 31

19
monday

20
tuesday

21
wednesday

22
thursday

23
friday

24
saturday

New Moon ●

25
sunday

Mothering Sunday (England)

April
s m t w t f s
1 2 3 4 5 6 7
8 9 10 11 12 13 14
15 16 17 18 19 20 21
22 23 24 25 26 27 28
29 30

THERE IS A FINE LINE WHERE THE SKY TOUCHES THE OCEAN.
THAT IS WHAT GOD IS LIKE....
HE FOREVER RESTS ON THE HORIZON OF ALL OPPOSITES.

— *Paramahansa Yogananda*

Sunset, Salton Sea, California   Photograph by Carol Fuegi

DIVINE LOVE IS THE FORCE EXPRESSED IN THE BALANCE,
CREATED BY THE MAGNETIC FORCE WHICH KEEPS STELLAR SYSTEMS
AND FLOATING UNIVERSES SWIMMING IN ETERNAL RHYTHM.

— *Paramahansa Yogananda*

Comet Hale-Bopp and sand dune, Death Valley National Park, California   Photograph by Michael Frye

March

s	m	t	w	t	f	s
				1	2	3
4	5	6	7	8	9	10
11	12	13	14	15	16	17
18	19	20	21	22	23	24
25	26	27	28	29	30	31

March/April

26
monday

27
tuesday

28
wednesday

29
thursday

30
friday

31
saturday

1
sunday

First Quarter ◖ *Daylight Savings Begins (U.S. and Canada)*

April

s	m	t	w	t	f	s
1	2	3	4	5	6	7
8	9	10	11	12	13	14
15	16	17	18	19	20	21
22	23	24	25	26	27	28
29	30					

April

April

s m t w t f s
1 2 3 4 5 6 7
8 9 10 11 12 13 14
15 16 17 18 19 20 21
22 23 24 25 26 27 28
29 30

2
monday

3
tuesday

4
wednesday

5
thursday

6
friday

7
saturday

Full Moon ○

8
sunday

Passover Begins

May

s m t w t f s
        1 2 3 4 5
6 7 8 9 10 11 12
13 14 15 16 17 18 19
20 21 22 23 24 25 26
27 28 29 30 31

THE BLOSSOMS OF LIFE IN THE GARDEN OF EARTHLY EXISTENCE
ARE ENCHANTING TO BEHOLD. BUT SOMEWHERE THERE IS A FOUNT
OF BEAUTY AND INTELLIGENCE, EVEN MORE ENTHRALLING,
FROM WHICH WE HAVE COME AND INTO WHICH WE SHALL MERGE AGAIN.

—*Paramahansa Yogananda*

Feather star crinoids and soft coral, Madang, Papua New Guinea   Photograph by Fred Bavendam/Minden Pictures

SUCCESS COMES BY GRASPING IT, AND NOT BY JUST WAITING FOR IT.

—*Paramahansa Yogananda*

Yellow-headed blackbird, Market Lake, Idaho   Photograph by John Gerlach/DRK Photo

April

s	m	t	w	t	f	s
1	2	3	4	5	6	7
8	9	10	11	12	13	14
15	16	17	18	19	20	21
22	23	24	25	26	27	28
29	30					

April

9
monday

10
tuesday

11
wednesday

12
thursday

13
friday

Good Friday

14
saturday

15
sunday

Last Quarter ◑   *Easter Sunday*

May

s	m	t	w	t	f	s
		1	2	3	4	5
6	7	8	9	10	11	12
13	14	15	16	17	18	19
20	21	22	23	24	25	26
27	28	29	30	31		

April

April

s	m	t	w	t	f	s
1	2	3	4	5	6	7
8	9	10	11	12	13	14
15	16	17	18	19	20	21
22	23	24	25	26	27	28
29	30					

16
monday

Easter Monday (All except U.S. and Scotland)

17
tuesday

18
wednesday

19
thursday

20
friday

21
saturday

22
sunday

May

s	m	t	w	t	f	s
		1	2	3	4	5
6	7	8	9	10	11	12
13	14	15	16	17	18	19
20	21	22	23	24	25	26
27	28	29	30	31		

I WILL BE THE WAKING OF THE DAWN,
AND BURST FORTH WITH THE WARMING RAYS OF FRIENDSHIP.

—*Paramahansa Yogananda*

Sunrise at mouth of Santee River, South Carolina   Photograph by Tom Blagden/Larry Ulrich Stock

MATTER IS NOT ONLY "FROZEN" ENERGY
BUT ALSO THE "FROZEN" CONSCIOUSNESS OF GOD.

— *Paramahansa Yogananda*

Icicles, Lake Saimaa, Finland   Photograph by Tapani Räsänen

April

s	m	t	w	t	f	s
	1	2	3	4	5	6	7
8	9	10	11	12	13	14
15	16	17	18	19	20	21
22	23	24	25	26	27	28
29	30					

April

23
monday

New Moon ●   *St. George's Day (England)*

24
tuesday

25
wednesday

ANZAC Day (Aus. and N.Z.)

26
thursday

27
friday

28
saturday

29
sunday

May

s	m	t	w	t	f	s
		1	2	3	4	5
6	7	8	9	10	11	12
13	14	15	16	17	18	19
20	21	22	23	24	25	26
27	28	29	30	31		

April/May

April

s	m	t	w	t	f	s
1	2	3	4	5	6	7
8	9	10	11	12	13	14
15	16	17	18	19	20	21
22	23	24	25	26	27	28
29	30					

30
monday

First Quarter ◗

1
tuesday

2
wednesday

3
thursday

National Day of Prayer

4
friday

5
saturday

6
sunday

May

s	m	t	w	t	f	s
		1	2	3	4	5
6	7	8	9	10	11	12
13	14	15	16	17	18	19
20	21	22	23	24	25	26
27	28	29	30	31		

LOVE...IS THE PROMPTINGS OF THE MOTHER EARTH
TO FEED HER MILK TO THE TENDER, THIRSTY ROOTS,
AND TO NURSE ALL LIFE.

— Paramahansa Yogananda

Plum trees and Hi gan-bana flowers, Saitama-Prefecture, Japan   Photograph by Jun Ogawa

MAY ALL...WHO HAVE BEEN NURTURED BY A MOTHER'S LOVE
BE THEMSELVES FILLED WITH A MOTHER'S AFFECTION,
WHICH IS UNCONDITIONAL LOVE, AND EXPRESS IT TOWARD OTHERS.

— *Paramahansa Yogananda*

Giraffe mother and newborn calf, Smburu Park, Kenya   Photograph by Karl Ammann

May

s	m	t	w	t	f	s
		1	2	3	4	5
6	7	8	9	10	11	12
13	14	15	16	17	18	19
20	21	22	23	24	25	26
27	28	29	30	31		

May

7
monday

Full Moon ◯   May Day Bank Holiday (U.K.)

8
tuesday

9
wednesday

10
thursday

Sri Yukteswar's Birthday

11
friday

12
saturday

13
sunday

Mother's Day (U.S., Aus. and N.Z.)

June

s	m	t	w	t	f	s
					1	2
3	4	5	6	7	8	9
10	11	12	13	14	15	16
17	18	19	20	21	22	23
24	25	26	27	28	29	30

May

May

s	m	t	w	t	f	s
		1	2	3	4	5
6	7	8	9	10	11	12
13	14	15	16	17	18	19
20	21	22	23	24	25	26
27	28	29	30	31		

14
monday

15
tuesday

Last Quarter ◑

16
wednesday

17
thursday

18
friday

19
saturday

20
sunday

June

s	m	t	w	t	f	s
					1	2
3	4	5	6	7	8	9
10	11	12	13	14	15	16
17	18	19	20	21	22	23
24	25	26	27	28	29	30

FILL THIS LIFE THAT WE LOVE SO DEARLY
WITH THE NECTAR OF PERPETUAL SOUL-PEACE.

— *Paramahansa Yogananda*

Pink primula with water droplets, Wassenaar, Netherlands   Photograph by Rosemary Calvert/Planet Earth Pictures Ltd

SOMETIMES THE POWER OF GOD COMES LIKE AN OCEAN
AND SURGES THROUGH YOUR BEING IN GREAT BOUNDLESS WAVES,
SWEEPING AWAY ALL MENTAL OBSTACLES.

— *Paramahansa Yogananda*

Wave in early morning light, Waimea Bay, Hawaii   Photograph by Woody Woodworth

s	m	t	w	t	f	s
		1	2	3	4	5
6	7	8	9	10	11	12
13	14	15	16	17	18	19
20	21	22	23	24	25	26
27	28	29	30	31		

May

21
monday

Victoria Day (Canada)

22
tuesday

New Moon ●

23
wednesday

24
thursday

25
friday

26
saturday

27
sunday

June

s	m	t	w	t	f	s
					1	2
3	4	5	6	7	8	9
10	11	12	13	14	15	16
17	18	19	20	21	22	23
24	25	26	27	28	29	30

May/June

May

s	m	t	w	t	f	s
		1	2	3	4	5
6	7	8	9	10	11	12
13	14	15	16	17	18	19
20	21	22	23	24	25	26
27	28	29	30	31		

28
monday

Memorial Day   Spring Bank Holiday (U.K.)

29
tuesday

First Quarter ◗

30
wednesday

31
thursday

1
friday

2
saturday

3
sunday

June

s	m	t	w	t	f	s
					1	2
3	4	5	6	7	8	9
10	11	12	13	14	15	16
17	18	19	20	21	22	23
24	25	26	27	28	29	30

CALMNESS IS ONE OF THE ATTRIBUTES OF THE IMMORTALITY WITHIN YOU.

— *Paramahansa Yogananda*

Sunset, Kornati National Park, Croatia, on the Adriatic Sea   Photograph by Matevz Lenarcic

IF WE ARE ATTUNED TO GOD,
OUR PERCEPTION IS LIMITLESS, PERVADING EVERYWHERE
IN THE OCEANIC FLOW OF THE DIVINE PRESENCE.

— *Paramahansa Yogananda*

Camels in the Sam Sand Dunes, Rajasthan, India   Photograph by Raoul Slater

June

s	m	t	w	t	f	s
					1	2
3	4	5	6	7	8	9
10	11	12	13	14	15	16
17	18	19	20	21	22	23
24	25	26	27	28	29	30

June

Queen's Birthday (N.Z.)

4
monday

5
tuesday

Full Moon ○

6
wednesday

7
thursday

8
friday

9
saturday

10
sunday

July

s	m	t	w	t	f	s
1	2	3	4	5	6	7
8	9	10	11	12	13	14
15	16	17	18	19	20	21
22	23	24	25	26	27	28
29	30	31				

June

June

s	m	t	w	t	f	s
					1	2
3	4	5	6	7	8	9
10	11	12	13	14	15	16
17	18	19	20	21	22	23
24	25	26	27	28	29	30

11
monday

Queen's Birthday (Aus.)

12
tuesday

13
wednesday

Last Quarter ◗

14
thursday

15
friday

16
saturday

17
sunday

Father's Day

July

s	m	t	w	t	f	s
1	2	3	4	5	6	7
8	9	10	11	12	13	14
15	16	17	18	19	20	21
22	23	24	25	26	27	28
29	30	31				

ALL THE DIFFICULTIES THAT VISIT YOU
ARE MEANT ONLY TO STIMULATE YOU TO HIGHER ACHIEVEMENTS.

— *Paramahansa Yogananda*

Lion, Masai Mara, Kenya   Photograph by Windland Rice/Jeff Foott Productions

BE TRANSPARENT LIKE THE GEMS....
THINKING AND PERCEPTION SHOULD HAVE GEMLIKE CLARITY
THAT WILL UNDISTORTEDLY REFLECT THE DIVINE MIND.

— *Paramahansa Yogananda*

Dew on sweet pea tendril, and sapphire chrysanthemums, Portland, Oregon   Photograph by Steve Terrill/The Stock Market

June

s	m	t	w	t	f	s
					1	2
3	4	5	6	7	8	9
10	11	12	13	14	15	16
17	18	19	20	21	22	23
24	25	26	27	28	29	30

June

18
monday

19
tuesday

20
wednesday

21
thursday

New Moon ●   *Total Solar Eclipse*

22
friday

23
saturday

24
sunday

July

s	m	t	w	t	f	s
1	2	3	4	5	6	7
8	9	10	11	12	13	14
15	16	17	18	19	20	21
22	23	24	25	26	27	28
29	30	31				

June/July

June

s	m	t	w	t	f	s
					1	2
3	4	5	6	7	8	9
10	11	12	13	14	15	16
17	18	19	20	21	22	23
24	25	26	27	28	29	30

25
monday

26
tuesday

27
wednesday

First Quarter ◗

28
thursday

29
friday

30
saturday

1
sunday

July

s	m	t	w	t	f	s
	1	2	3	4	5	6	7
8	9	10	11	12	13	14
15	16	17	18	19	20	21
22	23	24	25	26	27	28
29	30	31				

BECAUSE WE DON'T CONCENTRATE WITHIN,
WE ARE MYSTIFIED BY THE IMPRINTS OF THE INVISIBLE SPIRIT IN NATURE.

— *Paramahansa Yogananda*

Evening reflection of sandstone cliff in pond, central Wyoming   Photograph by John Eastcott and Yva Momatiuk

ALL KNOWLEDGE COMES FROM THE INNER SOURCE, FROM THE LIMITLESS SOUL....
IN YOU LIES THE SEAT OF INFINITE KNOWLEDGE.

— *Paramahansa Yogananda*

Chinese lanterns, Issaquah, Washington   Photograph by Darrell Gulin

July

s	m	t	w	t	f	s
1	2	3	4	5	6	7
8	9	10	11	12	13	14
15	16	17	18	19	20	21
22	23	24	25	26	27	28
29	30	31				

July

2
monday

Canada Day (Canada)

3
tuesday

4
wednesday

Independence Day

5
thursday

Full Moon ○

6
friday

7
saturday

8
sunday

August

s	m	t	w	t	f	s
			1	2	3	4
5	6	7	8	9	10	11
12	13	14	15	16	17	18
19	20	21	22	23	24	25
26	27	28	29	30	31	

July

9
monday

10
tuesday

11
wednesday

12
thursday

13
friday

Last Quarter ◗

14
saturday

15
sunday

July

s	m	t	w	t	f	s
1	2	3	4	5	6	7
8	9	10	11	12	13	14
15	16	17	18	19	20	21
22	23	24	25	26	27	28
29	30	31				

August

s	m	t	w	t	f	s
				1	2	3	4
5	6	7	8	9	10	11
12	13	14	15	16	17	18
19	20	21	22	23	24	25
26	27	28	29	30	31	

WATCH THE ETERNAL CIRCLE OF RIPPLING PEACE AROUND YOU.
THE MORE YOU WATCH INTENTLY,
THE MORE YOU WILL FEEL THE WAVELETS OF PEACE.

— Paramahansa Yogananda

Reddish egret, Ding Darling National Wildlife Refuge, Sanibel Island, Florida   Photograph by Arthur Morris

EACH FLOWER IS A DIVINE TEMPLE
IN WHICH THE DIVINE ONE COMES TO US.

— *Paramahansa Yogananda*

Iris detail, Maryland   Photograph by *Beth Kingsley Hawkins*

July

s	m	t	w	t	f	s
	1	2	3	4	5	6	7
8	9	10	11	12	13	14
15	16	17	18	19	20	21
22	23	24	25	26	27	28
29	30	31				

July

16
monday

17
tuesday

18
wednesday

19
thursday

20
friday

New Moon ●

21
saturday

22
sunday

August

s	m	t	w	t	f	s
				1	2	3	4
5	6	7	8	9	10	11
12	13	14	15	16	17	18
19	20	21	22	23	24	25
26	27	28	29	30	31	

July

July

s	m	t	w	t	f	s
1	2	3	4	5	6	7
8	9	10	11	12	13	14
15	16	17	18	19	20	21
22	23	24	25	26	27	28
29	30	31				

23
monday

24
tuesday

25
wednesday

Mahavatar Babaji Commemoration Day

26
thursday

27
friday

First Quarter ◑

28
saturday

29
sunday

August

s	m	t	w	t	f	s
				1	2	3	4
5	6	7	8	9	10	11
12	13	14	15	16	17	18
19	20	21	22	23	24	25
26	27	28	29	30	31	

IT IS THE DIVINE MOTHER
WHO HAS TAKEN FORM TO SERVE YOU....
SHE LETS YOU THINK THAT YOUR VISIBLE MOTHER LOVES YOU,
WHILE IT IS REALLY HER LOVE WHICH IS BEING EXPRESSED.

— *Paramahansa Yogananda*

Wild mustang mare and foal, Pryor Mountain Wild Horse Range, Montana
Photograph by John Eastcott and Yva Momatiuk

THE MAGNIFICENT PAINTING OF CREATION
STRETCHES ACROSS THE INFINITE CANVAS OF TIME AND SPACE.

— *Paramahansa Yogananda*

Sunset, Manado Tua Marine National Park, Indonesia   Photograph by Fred Bavendam/Minden Pictures

July

s	m	t	w	t	f	s
	1	2	3	4	5	6	7
8	9	10	11	12	13	14
15	16	17	18	19	20	21
22	23	24	25	26	27	28
29	30	31				

July/August

30
monday

31
tuesday

1
wednesday

2
thursday

3
friday

Full Moon ○

4
saturday

5
sunday

August

s	m	t	w	t	f	s
				1	2	3	4
5	6	7	8	9	10	11
12	13	14	15	16	17	18
19	20	21	22	23	24	25
26	27	28	29	30	31	

August

August

s	m	t	w	t	f	s
			1	2	3	4
5	6	7	8	9	10	11
12	13	14	15	16	17	18
19	20	21	22	23	24	25
26	27	28	29	30	31	

6
monday

Bank Holiday (Scotland)   *Civic Holiday (Canada)*

7
tuesday

8
wednesday

9
thursday

10
friday

11
saturday

12
sunday

Janmashtami   *Last Quarter* ◐

September

s	m	t	w	t	f	s
						1
2	3	4	5	6	7	8
9	10	11	12	13	14	15
16	17	18	19	20	21	22
23/30	24	25	26	27	28	29

WHEN YOU EXPERIENCE...DIVINE LOVE,
YOU WILL SEE NO DIFFERENCE BETWEEN FLOWER AND BEAST,
BETWEEN ONE HUMAN BEING AND ANOTHER.
YOU WILL COMMUNE WITH ALL NATURE.

— *Paramahansa Yogananda*

Bengal tiger among water lilies, Safari Park, Bangkok, Thailand   Photograph by Martin Harvey/NHPA

ANY TIME YOU BECOME FASCINATED BY SOME MATERIAL CREATION,
CLOSE YOUR EYES, LOOK WITHIN, AND CONTEMPLATE ITS SOURCE.

— *Paramahansa Yogananda*

Encrusting sponge detail, Sangalakki Island, Indonesia   Photograph by Burt Jones and Maurine Shimlock

August

s	m	t	w	t	f	s
			1	2	3	4
5	6	7	8	9	10	11
12	13	14	15	16	17	18
19	20	21	22	23	24	25
26	27	28	29	30	31	

13
monday

14
tuesday

15
wednesday

16
thursday

17
friday

18
saturday

New Moon ●

19
sunday

September

s	m	t	w	t	f	s
						1
2	3	4	5	6	7	8
9	10	11	12	13	14	15
16	17	18	19	20	21	22
23 30	24	25	26	27	28	29

August

August

s	m	t	w	t	f	s
			1	2	3	4
5	6	7	8	9	10	11
12	13	14	15	16	17	18
19	20	21	22	23	24	25
26	27	28	29	30	31	

20
monday

21
tuesday

22
wednesday

23
thursday

24
friday

25
saturday

First Quarter ◗

26
sunday

September

s	m	t	w	t	f	s
						1
2	3	4	5	6	7	8
9	10	11	12	13	14	15
16	17	18	19	20	21	22
23 30	24	25	26	27	28	29

THE BEAUTY OF NATURE IS LIKE A FOUNTAIN.
YOU SEE THE BEAUTY OF THE SPRAY, BUT...NOT THE SUBTLE INNER BEAUTY,
NOR THE POWER THAT GIVES THAT BEAUTY TO NATURE.

— *Paramahansa Yogananda*

Common tern fishing, Lake Saimaa, Finland   Photograph by Tapani Räsänen

THE EMERGENCE OF NATURE, STONES, METALS, AND SO FORTH,
ARE THE FIRST SYMBOLS OF GOD'S BEAUTY.

— *Paramahansa Yogananda*

Mexican crazy lace agate, Sierra Santa Lucia Mountains, Mexico   Photograph by Alan Caddey

August

s	m	t	w	t	f	s
				1	2	3	4
5	6	7	8	9	10	11
12	13	14	15	16	17	18
19	20	21	22	23	24	25
26	27	28	29	30	31	

27
monday

Summer Bank Holiday (U.K. except Scotland)

28
tuesday

29
wednesday

30
thursday

31
friday

1
saturday

2
sunday

Full Moon ○

September

s	m	t	w	t	f	s
						1
2	3	4	5	6	7	8
9	10	11	12	13	14	15
16	17	18	19	20	21	22
23 30	24	25	26	27	28	29

September

3
monday

September

s m t w t f s
                    1
2 3 4 5 6 7 8
9 10 11 12 13 14 15
16 17 18 19 20 21 22
23 30 24 25 26 27 28 29

Labor Day (U.S. and Canada)

4
tuesday

5
wednesday

6
thursday

7
friday

8
saturday

9
sunday

October

s m t w t f s
      1 2 3 4 5 6
7 8 9 10 11 12 13
14 15 16 17 18 19 20
21 22 23 24 25 26 27
28 29 30 31

CHEERFUL COLORS ALWAYS CREATE HAPPINESS IN THE MIND.

— *Paramahansa Yogananda*

Stream near Lake Superior, Michigan   Photograph by Larry Michael

IN EVERY ASPECT OF MATTER IS EVIDENCE
OF THE ORIGINALITY...OF THAT COSMIC INTELLIGENCE.

— Paramahansa Yogananda

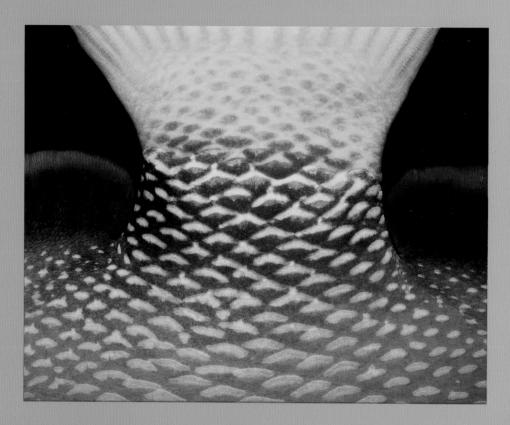

Tail of queen angelfish, Bahama Islands   Photograph by Jeff Rotman

September

s m t w t f s
                1
2 3 4 5 6 7 8
9 10 11 12 13 14 15
16 17 18 19 20 21 22
23/30 24 25 26 27 28 29

September

10
monday

Last Quarter ◑

11
tuesday

12
wednesday

13
thursday

14
friday

15
saturday

16
sunday

October

s m t w t f s
        1 2 3 4 5 6
7 8 9 10 11 12 13
14 15 16 17 18 19 20
21 22 23 24 25 26 27
28 29 30 31

September

17
monday

September

s m t w t f s
1
2 3 4 5 6 7 8
9 10 11 12 13 14 15
16 17 18 19 20 21 22
23/30 24 25 26 27 28 29

New Moon ●

18
tuesday

Rosh Hashanah

19
wednesday

20
thursday

21
friday

22
saturday

23
sunday

October

s m t w t f s
1 2 3 4 5 6
7 8 9 10 11 12 13
14 15 16 17 18 19 20
21 22 23 24 25 26 27
28 29 30 31

THROUGH THE PORTALS OF SILENCE
THE HEALING SUN OF WISDOM AND PEACE WILL SHINE UPON YOU.

— *Paramahansa Yogananda*

Wading bird at sunset, Brigantine National Wildlife Refuge, New Jersey   Photograph by Arthur Morris

BE A DIFFERENT INDIVIDUAL,
EXPRESSING THE VERY BEST OF YOUR OWN UNIQUE NATURE.

— *Paramahansa Yogananda*

Stone on beach, Greek Island of Chios   Photograph by Adriano Turcatti

September

s m t w t f s
                1
2 3 4 5 6 7 8
9 10 11 12 13 14 15
16 17 18 19 20 21 22
23 30 24 25 26 27 28 29

September

24
monday

First Quarter ◐

25
tuesday

26
wednesday

Lahiri Mahasaya's Mahasamadhi

27
thursday

Yom Kippur

28
friday

29
saturday

30
sunday

Lahiri Mahasaya's Birthday

October

s m t w t f s
        1 2 3 4 5 6
7 8 9 10 11 12 13
14 15 16 17 18 19 20
21 22 23 24 25 26 27
28 29 30 31

October

October

s	m	t	w	t	f	s
		1	2	3	4	5	6
7	8	9	10	11	12	13
14	15	16	17	18	19	20
21	22	23	24	25	26	27
28	29	30	31			

1
monday

2
tuesday

Full Moon ○

3
wednesday

4
thursday

5
friday

6
saturday

7
sunday

November

s	m	t	w	t	f	s
					1	2	3
4	5	6	7	8	9	10
11	12	13	14	15	16	17
18	19	20	21	22	23	24
25	26	27	28	29	30	

WHEN YOU ARE CALM AND AT PEACE WITHIN, YOU LOVE EVERYONE
AND FEEL FRIENDLY TOWARD ALL.

— *Paramahansa Yogananda*

Bird with reflection of giraffe, South Africa   Photograph by Steve Bloom/Masterfile

THE NATURE OF MATTER IS CHANGE.
THE NATURE OF SPIRIT IS CHANGELESSNESS.

— *Paramahansa Yogananda*

Cecropia tree leaf detail, Guyana, South America   Photograph by Jan Vermeer

October

s m t w t f s
　　1　2　3　4　5　6
7　8　9　10　11　12　13
14　15　16　17　18　19　20
21　22　23　24　25　26　27
28　29　30　31

Columbus Day　　*Thanksgiving Day (Canada)*

Last Quarter ◗

October

8
monday

9
tuesday

10
wednesday

11
thursday

12
friday

13
saturday

14
sunday

November

s m t w t f s
　　　　　1　2　3
4　5　6　7　8　9　10
11　12　13　14　15　16　17
18　19　20　21　22　23　24
25　26　27　28　29　30

October

October

s	m	t	w	t	f	s
	1	2	3	4	5	6
7	8	9	10	11	12	13
14	15	16	17	18	19	20
21	22	23	24	25	26	27
28	29	30	31			

15
monday

16
tuesday

New Moon ●

17
wednesday

18
thursday

19
friday

20
saturday

21
sunday

November

s	m	t	w	t	f	s
					1	2	3
4	5	6	7	8	9	10
11	12	13	14	15	16	17
18	19	20	21	22	23	24
25	26	27	28	29	30	

On the lotus leaf of your life
is trembling the dewdrop of God's consciousness. Realize that!
Find the connection between the dewdrop
and its Infinite Source and you shall find Him.

— *Paramahansa Yogananda*

Lotus, Ibaraki-Prefecture, Japan   Photograph by Jun Ogawa

MANIFEST ON THE SURFACE OF YOUR LIFE
THE DIVINE POWER WITHIN YOU.

— *Paramahansa Yogananda*

Weddell's seal at air hole, Antarctica   Photograph by Kim Westerkov/Tony Stone Images

October

s	m	t	w	t	f	s
		1	2	3	4	5	6
7	8	9	10	11	12	13
14	15	16	17	18	19	20
21	22	23	24	25	26	27
28	29	30	31			

October

22
monday

Labour Day (N.Z.)

23
tuesday

First Quarter ◑

24
wednesday

25
thursday

26
friday

27
saturday

28
sunday

Daylight Savings Ends (U.S. and Canada)

November

s	m	t	w	t	f	s
					1	2	3
4	5	6	7	8	9	10
11	12	13	14	15	16	17
18	19	20	21	22	23	24
25	26	27	28	29	30	

October/November

29
monday

30
tuesday

31
wednesday

Halloween   *Full Moon* ○

1
thursday

2
friday

3
saturday

4
sunday

October

s	m	t	w	t	f	s
		1	2	3	4	5	6
7	8	9	10	11	12	13
14	15	16	17	18	19	20
21	22	23	24	25	26	27
28	29	30	31			

November

s	m	t	w	t	f	s
					1	2	3
4	5	6	7	8	9	10
11	12	13	14	15	16	17
18	19	20	21	22	23	24
25	26	27	28	29	30	

A SECRET FORCE IS AT WORK
TRYING TO CARRY OUT A PLAN—A MORAL, SPIRITUAL PLAN
TO BRING ORDER OUT OF THE SEEMING CHAOS OF CREATION.

—*Paramahansa Yogananda*

Leaves in swirling water, Sir Richard Squires Provincial Park, Newfoundland   Photograph by Dale Wilson/Masterfile

SURROUND YOURSELF WITH THE BEST COMPANY,
THOSE WHO WILL INSPIRE YOU
AND STRENGTHEN YOUR DISCRIMINATION AND WILL POWER.

— *Paramahansa Yogananda*

Bullfinches on a mountain ash, Sweden   Photograph by Jan Töve Johansson/Planet Earth Pictures Ltd

November

s	m	t	w	t	f	s
				1	2	3
4	5	6	7	8	9	10
11	12	13	14	15	16	17
18	19	20	21	22	23	24
25	26	27	28	29	30	

November

5
monday

Guy Fawkes Day (England)

6
tuesday

7
wednesday

8
thursday

Last Quarter ◑

9
friday

10
saturday

11
sunday

Veterans Day   Remembrance Day (Canada)

December

s	m	t	w	t	f	s
						1
2	3	4	5	6	7	8
9	10	11	12	13	14	15
16	17	18	19	20	21	22
23 30	24 31	25	26	27	28	29

November

November
s m t w t f s
1 2 3
4 5 6 7 8 9 10
11 12 13 14 15 16 17
18 19 20 21 22 23 24
25 26 27 28 29 30

12
monday

Veterans Day (observed)

13
tuesday

14
wednesday

New Moon ●

15
thursday

16
friday

17
saturday

18
sunday

December
s m t w t f s
1
2 3 4 5 6 7 8
9 10 11 12 13 14 15
16 17 18 19 20 21 22
23 24 25 26 27 28 29
30 31

ONLY THOSE WHO PARTAKE OF THE HARMONY WITHIN THEIR SOULS
KNOW THE HARMONY THAT RUNS THROUGH NATURE.

— *Paramahansa Yogananda*

Sunrise on Lake Tolken, Sweden   Photograph by Jan Töve Johansson

WE WILL LEARN THE ANSWERS TO THE PUZZLES OF LIFE,
AND FIND THE SOLUTION TO ALL OUR DIFFICULTIES,
WHEN WE COME IN CONTACT WITH GOD.

— *Paramahansa Yogananda*

Brittle stars in tide pool, Monterey Bay, California   Photograph by Jeff Foott

November

s	m	t	w	t	f	s
				1	2	3
4	5	6	7	8	9	10
11	12	13	14	15	16	17
18	19	20	21	22	23	24
25	26	27	28	29	30	

November

19
monday

20
tuesday

21
wednesday

22
thursday

First Quarter ◑   *Thanksgiving*

23
friday

24
saturday

25
sunday

December

s	m	t	w	t	f	s
						1
2	3	4	5	6	7	8
9	10	11	12	13	14	15
16	17	18	19	20	21	22
23 / 30	24 / 31	25	26	27	28	29

November/December

November
s m t w t f s
              1 2 3
4 5 6 7 8 9 10
11 12 13 14 15 16 17
18 19 20 21 22 23 24
25 26 27 28 29 30

26
monday

27
tuesday

28
wednesday

29
thursday

30
friday

St. Andrew's Day (Scotland)   *Full Moon* ○

1
saturday

2
sunday

December
s m t w t f s
                    1
2 3 4 5 6 7 8
9 10 11 12 13 14 15
16 17 18 19 20 21 22
23 24 25 26 27 28 29
30 31

BREATHING THROUGH ALL THE PORES OF LIFE IS THE ONE LIFE.

— *Paramahansa Yogananda*

Autumn reflections and great blue heron, Moose Pond, New Hampshire
Photograph by John Eastcott and Yva Momatiuk / Masterfile

EVERYTHING IS SPIRIT—IN ESSENCE, THOUGH HIDDEN IN MANIFESTATION.
IF YOU HAD THE PERCEPTION, YOU WOULD SEE GOD IN EVERYTHING.

— *Paramahansa Yogananda*

Fluorescent cup coral, Monterey Bay, California   Photograph by Dan Welsh-Bon

December

s	m	t	w	t	f	s
						1
2	3	4	5	6	7	8
9	10	11	12	13	14	15
16	17	18	19	20	21	22
23/30	24/31	25	26	27	28	29

December

3
monday

4
tuesday

5
wednesday

6
thursday

7
friday

Last Quarter ◗

8
saturday

9
sunday

January

s	m	t	w	t	f	s
		1	2	3	4	5
6	7	8	9	10	11	12
13	14	15	16	17	18	19
20	21	22	23	24	25	26
27	28	29	30	31		

December

December

s	m	t	w	t	f	s
						1
2	3	4	5	6	7	8
9	10	11	12	13	14	15
16	17	18	19	20	21	22
23 30	24 31	25	26	27	28	29

10
monday

Hanukkah

11
tuesday

12
wednesday

13
thursday

14
friday

New Moon ●

15
saturday

16
sunday

January

s	m	t	w	t	f	s
		1	2	3	4	5
6	7	8	9	10	11	12
13	14	15	16	17	18	19
20	21	22	23	24	25	26
27	28	29	30	31		

As moving pictures are sustained by a beam of light
coming from the projection booth of a movie house,
so are all of us sustained by the Cosmic Beam,
the Divine Light pouring from the projection booth of Eternity.

—*Paramahansa Yogananda*

Falling snow, Kuusamo, Finland   Photograph by Hannu Hautala

WHATEVER YOU WANT TO DO, THINK ABOUT IT...THEN TAKE A LITTLE TIME;
DON'T JUMP INTO ANYTHING AT ONCE.

— *Paramahansa Yogananda*

Amazon leaf frog on a heliconia leaf, Amazonia, Peru   Photograph by Stephen Kirkpatrick

December

s m t w t f s
1
2 3 4 5 6 7 8
9 10 11 12 13 14 15
16 17 18 19 20 21 22
23/30 24/31 25 26 27 28 29

December

17
monday

18
tuesday

19
wednesday

20
thursday

21
friday

First Quarter ◑

22
saturday

23
sunday

January

s m t w t f s
1 2 3 4 5
6 7 8 9 10 11 12
13 14 15 16 17 18 19
20 21 22 23 24 25 26
27 28 29 30 31

December

December
s m t w t f s
                    1
2 3 4 5 6 7 8
9 10 11 12 13 14 15
16 17 18 19 20 21 22
23 24 25 26 27 28 29
30 31

24
monday

25
tuesday

Christmas

26
wednesday

Boxing Day (U.K., Canada, Aus., and N.Z.)

27
thursday

28
friday

29
saturday

30
sunday

Full Moon ○

January
s m t w t f s
          1 2 3 4 5
6 7 8 9 10 11 12
13 14 15 16 17 18 19
20 21 22 23 24 25 26
27 28 29 30 31

THE ONLY WORTHWHILE CHANGE, THE ONLY PERMANENT ADVANCE,
IS THE INNER EVOLUTION OF MAN TOWARD SPIRITUAL PERFECTION.

— *Paramahansa Yogananda*

Moon over chapel, Lofoten, Norway   Photograph by Asle Hjellbrekke

WHEN WE LOOK UPON ALL THE GOOD IN NATURE,
WE EXPERIENCE A FEELING OF TENDERNESS WITHIN US.

— *Paramahansa Yogananda*

Red grouse in heather at sunrise, Bransdale, North Yorkshire, United Kingdom   Photograph by Roy Glen

December

s	m	t	w	t	f	s
						1
2	3	4	5	6	7	8
9	10	11	12	13	14	15
16	17	18	19	20	21	22
23 30	24 31	25	26	27	28	29

December/January

31
monday

1
tuesday

New Year's Day

2
wednesday

3
thursday

4
friday

Bank Holiday (Scotland)

5
saturday

Last Quarter ◑   *Paramahansa Yogananda's Birthday*

6
sunday

January

s	m	t	w	t	f	s
			1	2	3	4	5
6	7	8	9	10	11	12
13	14	15	16	17	18	19
20	21	22	23	24	25	26
27	28	29	30	31		

ACKNOWLEDGMENTS

~

We wish to express our sincere appreciation to the following photographers and agencies who contributed to this year's *Inner Reflections* engagement calendar. Following a contributor's name, in parentheses, is the month and first day of the week where each photo appears.

Karl Ammann (5/7)

Fred Bavendam (4/2; 7/30)

Tom Blagden (4/16)

Steve Bloom (10/1)

Alan Caddey (8/27)

Rosemary Calvert (5/14)

Charles Crust (opening photo)

DRK Photo (4/9)

Claudia duPlessis (1/29)

John Eastcott/Yva Momatiuk
(6/25; 7/23; 11/26)

Jeff Foott (11/19)

Michael Frye (3/26)

Carol Fuegi (3/19)

John Gerlach (4/9)

Adam Gibbs (3/12)

Roy Glen (12/31)

Darrell Gulin (7/2)

Martin Harvey (8/6)

Hannu Hautala (12/10)

Beth Kingsley Hawkins (7/16)

Asle Hjellbrekke (2/26; 12/24)

Jan Töve Johansson (2/12; 11/5; 11/12)

Burt Jones/Maurine Shimlock
(front cover; 8/13)

Stephen Kirkpatrick (12/17)

Matevz Lenarcic (5/28)

G. Brad Lewis (2/19)

David Lyons (2/5)

Masterfile (10/1; 10/29; 11/26)

Larry Michael (9/3)

Minden Pictures (4/2; 7/30)

Arthur Morris (7/9; 9/17)

NHPA (8/6)

Rob Nunnington (1/8)

Jun Ogawa (4/30; 10/15)

Pat O'Hara (1/15)

Oxford Scientific Films Ltd (1/8)

Photo Researchers, Inc. (3/5)

Planet Earth Pictures Ltd (2/12; 5/14; 11/5)

Tapani Räsänen (4/23; 8/20)

Windland Rice (6/11)

Jeff Rotman (9/10)

Raoul Slater (1/22; 6/4)

The Stock Market (6/18)

Steve Terrill (6/18)

Tony Stone Images (10/22)

Adriano Turcatti (9/24)

Jan Vermeer (10/8)

Dan Welsh-Bon (12/3)

Kim Westerkov (10/22)

Dale Wilson (10/29)

Woody Woodworth (5/21)

Norbert Wu (1/1)

"THE IDEAL OF LOVE FOR GOD AND SERVICE TO HUMANITY FOUND FULL EXPRESSION IN THE LIFE OF PARAMAHANSA YOGANANDA....THOUGH THE MAJOR PART OF HIS LIFE WAS SPENT OUTSIDE INDIA, STILL HE TAKES HIS PLACE AMONG OUR GREAT SAINTS. HIS WORK CONTINUES TO GROW AND SHINE EVER MORE BRIGHTLY, DRAWING PEOPLE EVERYWHERE ON THE PATH OF THE PILGRIMAGE OF THE SPIRIT."

—from a tribute by the Government of India upon issuing a special commemorative stamp in honor of

PARAMAHANSA YOGANANDA
1893–1952

BORN IN NORTHERN INDIA IN 1893, Paramahansa Yogananda came to the United States in 1920 as a delegate to an international congress of religious leaders convening in Boston. He remained in the West for the better part of the next thirty-two years, until his passing in 1952. Reporting at that time on his life and work, a Los Angeles periodical wrote: "Yogananda made an outstanding cultural and spiritual contribution in furthering the cause of better understanding between East and West. He combined in a conspicuous degree the spiritual idealism of India with practical activity of the West....The centers he established, the great numbers he inspired to nobler living, and the ideals he planted in the common consciousness of humanity will ever remain a monument to his notable achievement."

Self-Realization Fellowship, the international nonprofit society founded by Paramahansa Yogananda in 1920, is dedicated to carrying on his spiritual and humanitarian work—fostering a spirit of greater harmony and understanding among those of all nations and faiths, and introducing to truth-seekers all over the world his universal teachings on the ancient science of Yoga.

Paramahansa Yogananda's life story, *Autobiography of a Yogi*, is considered a modern spiritual classic. It has been translated into eighteen languages and is widely used in college and university courses. A perennial best-seller since it was first published more than fifty years ago, the book has found its way into the hearts of readers around the world.

An introductory booklet about the life and teachings of Paramahansa Yogananda and a book catalog are available upon request.

SELF-REALIZATION FELLOWSHIP
3880 San Rafael Avenue • Los Angeles, California 90065-3298
Telephone (323) 225-2471 • Fax (323) 225-5088
http://www.yogananda-srf.org

IMPORTANT NUMBERS

NAME _____

ADDRESS _____

CITY _____

STATE AND ZIP _____

PHONE _____ FAX _____

E-MAIL _____

NAME _____

ADDRESS _____

CITY _____

STATE AND ZIP _____

PHONE _____ FAX _____

E-MAIL _____

NAME _____

ADDRESS _____

CITY _____

STATE AND ZIP _____

PHONE _____ FAX _____

E-MAIL _____

NAME _____

ADDRESS _____

CITY _____

STATE AND ZIP _____

PHONE _____ FAX _____

E-MAIL _____

IMPORTANT NUMBERS

NAME

ADDRESS

CITY

STATE AND ZIP

PHONE   FAX

E-MAIL

NAME

ADDRESS

CITY

STATE AND ZIP

PHONE   FAX

E-MAIL

NAME

ADDRESS

CITY

STATE AND ZIP

PHONE   FAX

E-MAIL

NAME

ADDRESS

CITY

STATE AND ZIP

PHONE   FAX

E-MAIL

IMPORTANT NUMBERS

NAME

ADDRESS

CITY

STATE AND ZIP

PHONE   FAX

E-MAIL

NAME

ADDRESS

CITY

STATE AND ZIP

PHONE   FAX

E-MAIL

NAME

ADDRESS

CITY

STATE AND ZIP

PHONE   FAX

E-MAIL

NAME

ADDRESS

CITY

STATE AND ZIP

PHONE   FAX

E-MAIL

NOTES

NOTES

2000

January
s	m	t	w	t	f	s
						1
2	3	4	5	6	7	8
9	10	11	12	13	14	15
16	17	18	19	20	21	22
23 30	24 31	25	26	27	28	29

February
s	m	t	w	t	f	s
		1	2	3	4	5
6	7	8	9	10	11	12
13	14	15	16	17	18	19
20	21	22	23	24	25	26
27	28	29				

March
s	m	t	w	t	f	s
			1	2	3	4
5	6	7	8	9	10	11
12	13	14	15	16	17	18
19	20	21	22	23	24	25
26	27	28	29	30	31	

April
s	m	t	w	t	f	s
						1
2	3	4	5	6	7	8
9	10	11	12	13	14	15
16	17	18	19	20	21	22
23 30	24	25	26	27	28	29

May
s	m	t	w	t	f	s
	1	2	3	4	5	6
7	8	9	10	11	12	13
14	15	16	17	18	19	20
21	22	23	24	25	26	27
28	29	30	31			

June
s	m	t	w	t	f	s
				1	2	3
4	5	6	7	8	9	10
11	12	13	14	15	16	17
18	19	20	21	22	23	24
25	26	27	28	29	30	

July
s	m	t	w	t	f	s
						1
2	3	4	5	6	7	8
9	10	11	12	13	14	15
16	17	18	19	20	21	22
23 30	24 31	25	26	27	28	29

August
s	m	t	w	t	f	s
		1	2	3	4	5
6	7	8	9	10	11	12
13	14	15	16	17	18	19
20	21	22	23	24	25	26
27	28	29	30	31		

September
s	m	t	w	t	f	s
					1	2
3	4	5	6	7	8	9
10	11	12	13	14	15	16
17	18	19	20	21	22	23
24	25	26	27	28	29	30

October
s	m	t	w	t	f	s
1	2	3	4	5	6	7
8	9	10	11	12	13	14
15	16	17	18	19	20	21
22	23	24	25	26	27	28
29	30	31				

November
s	m	t	w	t	f	s
			1	2	3	4
5	6	7	8	9	10	11
12	13	14	15	16	17	18
19	20	21	22	23	24	25
26	27	28	29	30		

December
s	m	t	w	t	f	s
					1	2
3	4	5	6	7	8	9
10	11	12	13	14	15	16
17	18	19	20	21	22	23
24 31	25	26	27	28	29	30

2002

January
s	m	t	w	t	f	s
		1	2	3	4	5
6	7	8	9	10	11	12
13	14	15	16	17	18	19
20	21	22	23	24	25	26
27	28	29	30	31		

February
s	m	t	w	t	f	s
					1	2
3	4	5	6	7	8	9
10	11	12	13	14	15	16
17	18	19	20	21	22	23
24	25	26	27	28		

March
s	m	t	w	t	f	s
					1	2
3	4	5	6	7	8	9
10	11	12	13	14	15	16
17	18	19	20	21	22	23
24 31	25	26	27	28	29	30

April
s	m	t	w	t	f	s
	1	2	3	4	5	6
7	8	9	10	11	12	13
14	15	16	17	18	19	20
21	22	23	24	25	26	27
28	29	30				

May
s	m	t	w	t	f	s
			1	2	3	4
5	6	7	8	9	10	11
12	13	14	15	16	17	18
19	20	21	22	23	24	25
26	27	28	29	30	31	

June
s	m	t	w	t	f	s
						1
2	3	4	5	6	7	8
9	10	11	12	13	14	15
16	17	18	19	20	21	22
23 30	24	25	26	27	28	29

July
s	m	t	w	t	f	s
	1	2	3	4	5	6
7	8	9	10	11	12	13
14	15	16	17	18	19	20
21	22	23	24	25	26	27
28	29	30	31			

August
s	m	t	w	t	f	s
				1	2	3
4	5	6	7	8	9	10
11	12	13	14	15	16	17
18	19	20	21	22	23	24
25	26	27	28	29	30	31

September
s	m	t	w	t	f	s
1	2	3	4	5	6	7
8	9	10	11	12	13	14
15	16	17	18	19	20	21
22	23	24	25	26	27	28
29	30					

October
s	m	t	w	t	f	s
		1	2	3	4	5
6	7	8	9	10	11	12
13	14	15	16	17	18	19
20	21	22	23	24	25	26
27	28	29	30	31		

November
s	m	t	w	t	f	s
					1	2
3	4	5	6	7	8	9
10	11	12	13	14	15	16
17	18	19	20	21	22	23
24	25	26	27	28	29	30

December
s	m	t	w	t	f	s
1	2	3	4	5	6	7
8	9	10	11	12	13	14
15	16	17	18	19	20	21
22	23	24	25	26	27	28
29	30	31				

2001

January

s	m	t	w	t	f	s
	1	2	3	4	5	6
7	8	9	10	11	12	13
14	15	16	17	18	19	20
21	22	23	24	25	26	27
28	29	30	31			

February

s	m	t	w	t	f	s
				1	2	3
4	5	6	7	8	9	10
11	12	13	14	15	16	17
18	19	20	21	22	23	24
25	26	27	28			

March

s	m	t	w	t	f	s
				1	2	3
4	5	6	7	8	9	10
11	12	13	14	15	16	17
18	19	20	21	22	23	24
25	26	27	28	29	30	31

April

s	m	t	w	t	f	s
1	2	3	4	5	6	7
8	9	10	11	12	13	14
15	16	17	18	19	20	21
22	23	24	25	26	27	28
29	30					

May

s	m	t	w	t	f	s
		1	2	3	4	5
6	7	8	9	10	11	12
13	14	15	16	17	18	19
20	21	22	23	24	25	26
27	28	29	30	31		

June

s	m	t	w	t	f	s
					1	2
3	4	5	6	7	8	9
10	11	12	13	14	15	16
17	18	19	20	21	22	23
24	25	26	27	28	29	30

July

s	m	t	w	t	f	s
1	2	3	4	5	6	7
8	9	10	11	12	13	14
15	16	17	18	19	20	21
22	23	24	25	26	27	28
29	30	31				

August

s	m	t	w	t	f	s
			1	2	3	4
5	6	7	8	9	10	11
12	13	14	15	16	17	18
19	20	21	22	23	24	25
26	27	28	29	30	31	

September

s	m	t	w	t	f	s
						1
2	3	4	5	6	7	8
9	10	11	12	13	14	15
16	17	18	19	20	21	22
23 30	24	25	26	27	28	29

October

s	m	t	w	t	f	s
	1	2	3	4	5	6
7	8	9	10	11	12	13
14	15	16	17	18	19	20
21	22	23	24	25	26	27
28	29	30	31			

November

s	m	t	w	t	f	s
				1	2	3
4	5	6	7	8	9	10
11	12	13	14	15	16	17
18	19	20	21	22	23	24
25	26	27	28	29	30	

December

s	m	t	w	t	f	s
						1
2	3	4	5	6	7	8
9	10	11	12	13	14	15
16	17	18	19	20	21	22
23 30	24 31	25	26	27	28	29